"Fishing time!"

Bully Frog From Pinnebog

Author: Jim Steinman
Co-Illustrators: Mike Smith
& Jim Steinman

There once was a Bully Frog
from Pinnebog.
He sat very grumpily
on an old bumpy log.

1

A day came along
when it was 100 degrees!
Bully Frog was hot
from his head to his knees.

Bully Frog gasped for air
and jumped up high.
Landing in the river
that was very close by.

Bully Frog did a canonball
to get rid of his sweat.
Bully Frog splashed Miss Tree Frog,
who is now soaking wet.

4

Bully Frog ribbited,
"Get out of my space!
I don't want to look
at your colorful face!"

Miss Tree Frog stared
and sat for a while,
with a very sad face
and no sign of a smile.

6

Miss Tree Frog swam
out of the way.
She answered back,
"Hey bully, I can't stay!"

7

Bully Frog said, "Whatever,"
and swam down the brook.
He then came upon
a fishing hook.

Bully Frog thought, "What is wiggling down to this hook?" From a distance a big bass was also taking a look.

9

A little brown worm
squirmed down the line.
Bully Frog yelled, "Don't bother me
this space is mine!"

10

The worm's eyes grew very big
and he started to shake.
Bully Frog ribbited, "Stop your shaki
for goodness sake!

Come a little closer
it's you I want to see,
I'll have a little nibble,
because you are bugging me."

12

Then with a swish in the water
and a great big yawn,
with one mighty chomp
Bully Frog and the worm were gone!

13

A tug on the line
a hook of the fin,
the fisherman pulled
the big bass in!

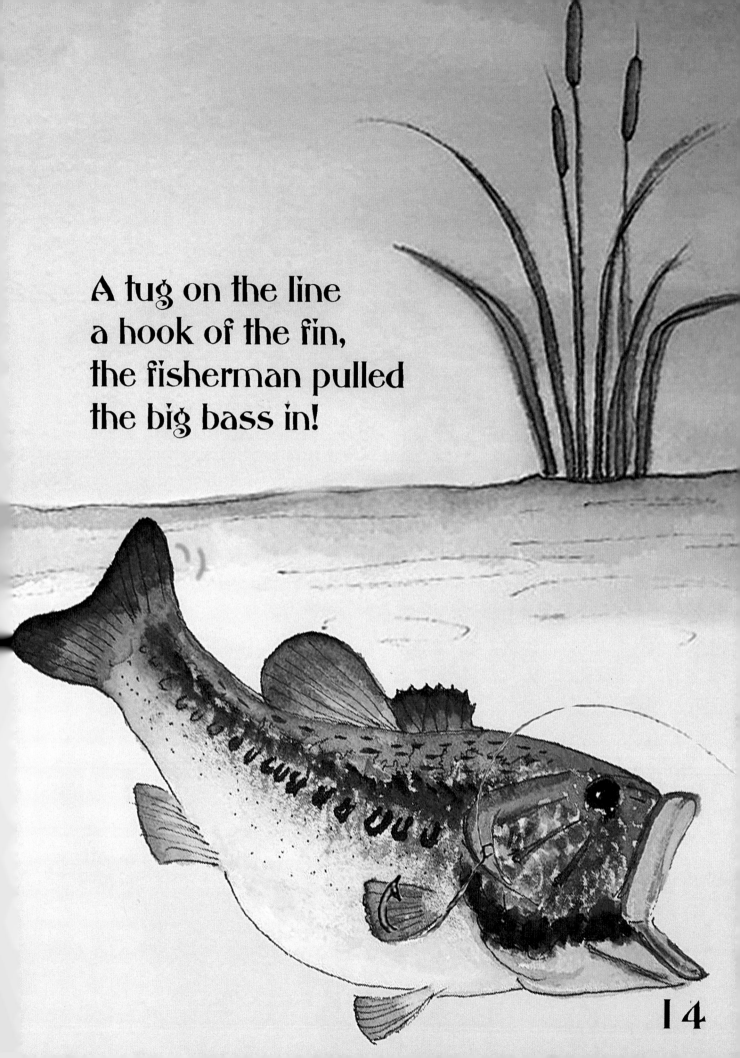

The big bass jerked
and started to squirm.
Then out popped the wiggly
little brown worm.

15

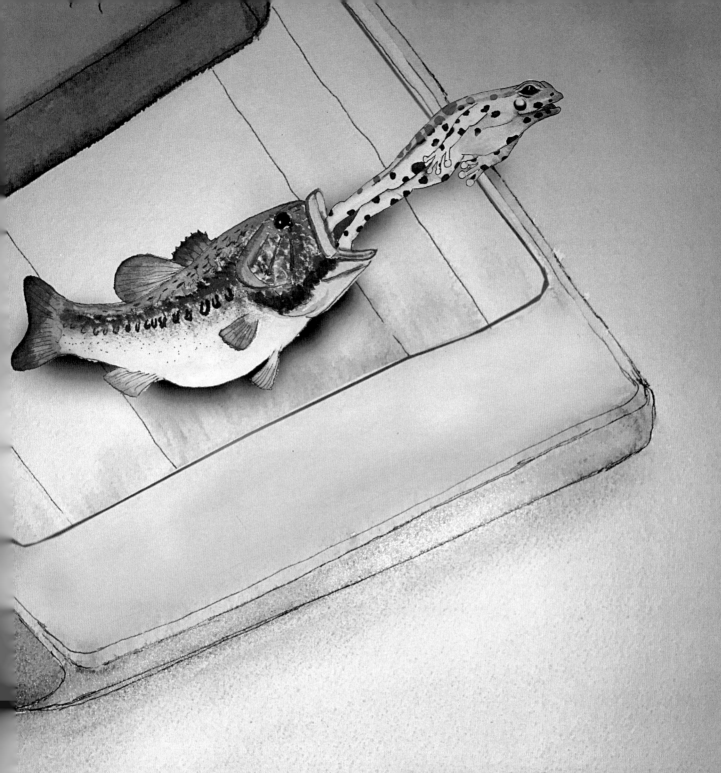

Then with a flip
and a splat in the boat.
Out flew Bully Frog
back in the moat.

Bully Frog was free
and back to his log.
Not a critter was crawling,
not even a frog.

Bully Frog From Pinnebog
changed his attitude.
From that day forward
he would never be rude.

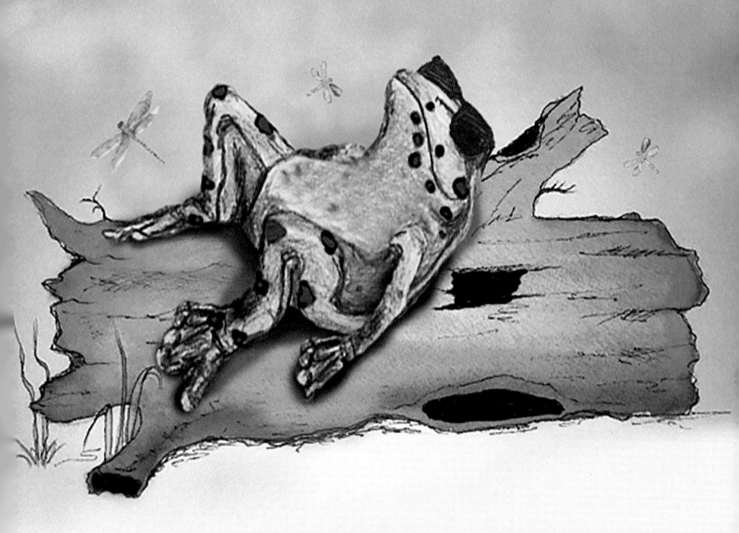

To my beautiful tadpoles,
Sarah, Skylar and Sadie,
who listened to me read
my stories over and over!
Love ya!
- Dad

To my friend and editor Amy M.,
We get to work together again!
What a great experience.
- J.S.

To my Illustrator Mike S.,
May we work on many more books together!
- J.S.

19

Author Jim Steinman's lifelong dream of writing books for children became a reality in 2018 with "Bully Frog from Pinnebog". Jim always enjoyed reading to his daughters, Sarah, Skylar and Sadie. It was while working as a Behavioral Interventionist at his girls' elementary school that the love of reading to children grew as well as his dream to create fun warm-hearted books that rhymed, were easy to read, and reinforced positive social skills. In addition to writing and illustrating, Jim enjoys spending time with his family, swimming, photography, and helping kids become better readers.

Made in the USA
Monee, IL
02 April 2020

Bully Frog From Pinnebog is a cute story about a Bully Frog that goes on an adventure and comes across a tree frog and a wiggly worm that Bully Frog bullies. A big bass gobbles him up and spits Bully Frog out to get a second chance on life, which changes him from that day on. This book is a children's fiction story that teaches about social skills for children everywhere.

ISBN 9780578644912 $15.99
51599 >
9 780578 644912

www.JimSteinmanPublications.com
Email: JimSteinmanPublications@gmail.com

What's Your Catholic IQ?

22 Faith Quizzes for All Ages

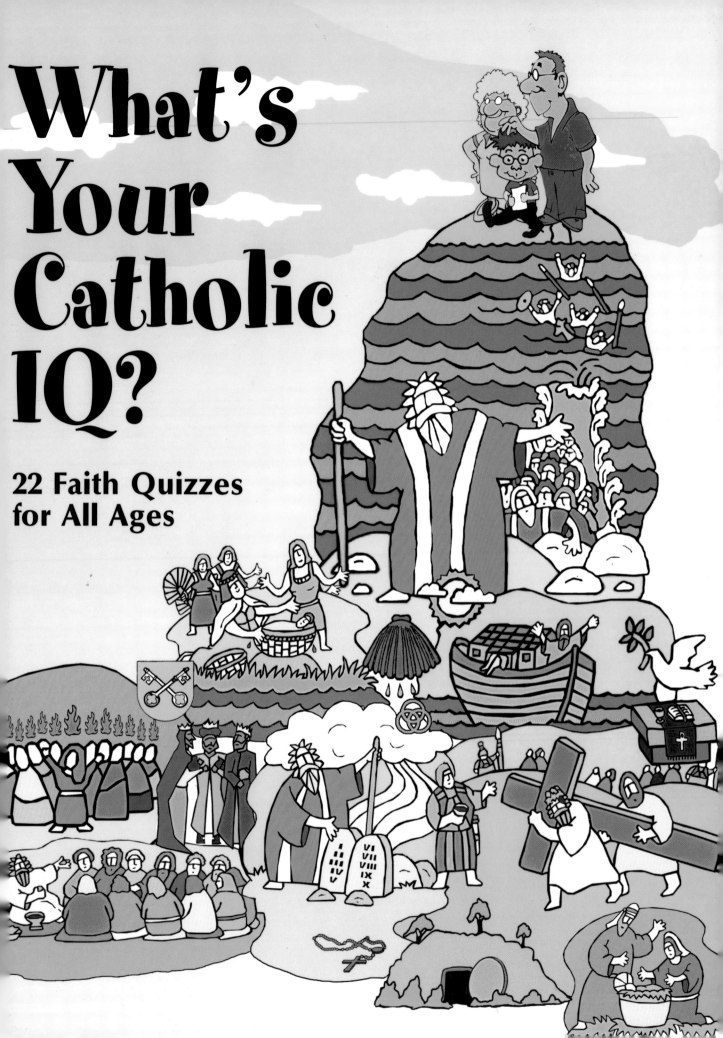